All the songs from the album

Shepherd Moons

GW00578003

© International Music Publications Limited
Southend Road, Woodford Green
Essex IG8 8HN, England

Foreword

*After Watermark was released - I was inundated with requests to talk about the lyrics. One part of me felt that
the lyrics should speak for themselves and that to 'explain' them would be like naming the colours of a painting while
forgetting to look at the picture. Another part of me wanted to acknowledge the genuine interest people were showing
and so I replied, haphazardly it seemed, to those who would have asked.*

*Here, with Shepherd Moons, I have, in response, provided some background to the songs in the hope that the
understanding of the songs may have some uniformity. This, of course, will go part of the way to explain them, for it
is also my hope that everyone who listens to them may hold their own interpretation. I have written about them by
searching for the genesis of the songs in diaries and notebooks I have kept and so the background has, as a result, the
flavour of a personal journal. It is, in a way, my Book of Days...*

Shepherd Moons

Two tiny new moons had been discovered. Shepherd Moons orbiting a ring of Saturn. Numbered, not named. Working ceaselessly, it seemed, to keep the particles of the ring together, much as a shepherd would guide his flock. Protectors both, 1980S26 and 1980S27 - either side of the F rings. Voyager had performed like a dream and sent their pictures to Earth. I marvelled at their diligence, a new mystery, poignant and beautiful. An unspoken glory to the rings of Saturn. The world had not known but all the time they were there, working tirelessly. Everyone had appreciated the spectacular beauty of Saturn, but where would the planet be without those precious, mis-shapen, miniature moons?

Caribbean Blue

It is much easier to imagine a beautiful place on a rainy day than to imagine a dreary one. It is a simple fact, often forgotten, that people may create something good merely by thinking it so. A day-dream is as rich a gift as any. Like Afer Ventus, the wind from Africa, or Eurus, the East wind, Boreas from the North or the gentle Zephyrus, the imagination is free and can choose and create its own journey. As with all dreams we reach for the ideal, and Caribbean Blue represents such a dream.

How Can I Keep from Singing?

This is based on an old Shaker hymn which I suggested as a suitable addition to the album, not only because of the beautiful melody, but the lyrical content seems as relevant today as it did 250 years ago when the hymn was written.

It is unfortunate that the Shakers are known to the world at large mainly for their ability to build and design beautiful furniture. The Shakers also wrote beautiful music and songs with which they glorified their joy in living. They lived very simple lives and their melodies reflect the beauty inherent in this simplicity.

It is not widely known that in 1846 the Shakers sent food to Ireland in an attempt to relieve the suffering during the famine, and this also held significance in our decision to arrange the piece.

Ebudae

I had come across Ebudae in Ariosto's classic tale of Orlando Furioso, the island thought to be intended as one of the Hebrides, referred to as the Dreadful Isle or the Isle Of Tears. I had fallen in love with the name, and when sometime later I was browsing through an old book of ancient maps, I was delighted to find Ebudae actually recorded and in this original form! The title of the song 'Ebudae' and the lyrics concern themselves with ancient sounds.

There are two 'voices' which work their way through the piece. The first voice concerns itself with the story - which is loosely based on the tradition of women weaving and chanting to the rhythm of their work. The second voice is a mixture of sounds and fragments of sounds half-invented, half-remembered from childhood. As is often the case, what one actually hears and what one thinks one hears can be two very different things. With this rhythmic section we try to capture those impressions.

Angeles

At times we ask for extraordinary things to happen in our lives and somehow, deep down, we believe that they will. Someone, somewhere, may have the power to help us - a Guardian Angel perhaps, some spiritual minder, a protector from life's darker moments.

Such a belief can be a comfort in life, an easy relationship with a world beyond our own. A gentle hand on your shoulder to guide you through, though not away from, the harder times

No Holly For Miss Quinn

A partner piece to Miss Clare Remembers (Watermark). No Holly For Miss Holly was prompted by another Miss Read story. The idyllic descriptions of country and village life and the simple portraits of those who peopled such settings had appeal to Enya. In composing this music she recaptures the naivety and innocence of an age and place far removed from the whirl and pressure of our sophisticated society and suggests that we need to dip into that world from time to time.

Book Of Days

I am collecting diaries more and more and I continue to be intrigued by the possibilities of each blank page - what will it hold? I experience a mixture of sadness and exuberance when I think of lives laid out on a page or in a book. Personal histories of great loves, of journeys exotic and wonderful, of loss, fear and tragedy, of dreams and simple wishes.

Evacuee

I remember her face. She told of how she had been an evacuee during the Second World War. As she told her story she began to cry like the girl she had been half a century ago. The pain of her separation from her parents registered with immediacy on her face. As a child she could not understand why she had to leave them, and the effect of this had stayed with her. The only hope she had as a child was a promise that they would all be together again.

Lothlórien

Sam felt as if he were inside a song when he described Lothlórien, the land of enchantment and wonder in J.R.R. Tolkien's 'Lord Of The Rings'. Lothlórien is as beautiful as a dream, as pure as the dawn of creation and as old as the beginning of time. Here, the leaves of the Mallorn trees in Autumn do not fall, but turn to gold.

Various translations and suggested origins of the name Lothlórien give us colourful and imaginative expressions such as 'the vale of the land of singers', 'the valley of the singing Gold' and 'Dreamflower'.

Marble Halls

An operatic piece originally scored by the Irish composer and baritone, Michael William Balfe (1808-1870). Marble Halls, or The Dream as it is also known, is from his 1843 opera The Bohemian Girl, which enjoyed great success during his lifetime. Balfe was once complimented by Strauss as being the Master of Melody. The Bohemian Girl, and in particular this song, is a favourite of both Enya and her mother.

Afer Ventus

The moment experienced when everything in life suddenly makes sense - when everything fits into place and we know why - is a rare moment, but it does happen. If we are lucky enough we can bathe in the brevity of that moment for it passes as quickly as it arrives. Like Joyce's 'Epiphanies' they can sometimes seem trivial, but are always crucial and revealing moments in our lives, delicate and fleeting.

In Afer Ventus it is those moments of pure enlightenment which are described.

Smaointe...(D 'Aodh Agus Do Mháire uí Dhúgain)

The story of the beach at Maragallen (The Plain of the Shelter) is that many years past, a great wave swept onto the land, crashing down upon the small church and graveyard, destroying the church. All who were in the church that day, perished.

It is in this same graveyard that Enya's grandparents are buried. Enya often talked to me of how she could see the graveyard as she walked along the shores of the Maragallen, and of how she felt her grandparents were watching over her and guiding her still. Memories of her childhood and days spent with them come to Enya when she walks there, memories which she will treasure always. I wrote Smaointe in response to these reflections. The word 'smaointe' literally translated means 'thoughts'.

Shepherd Moons

Music by Enya & Nicky Ryan

Slow and free

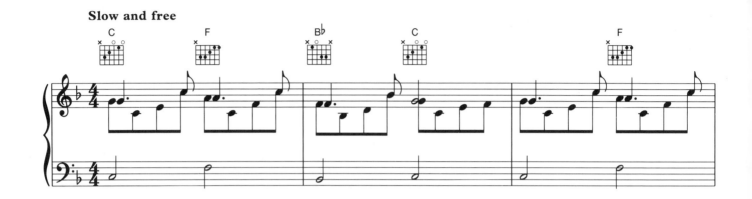

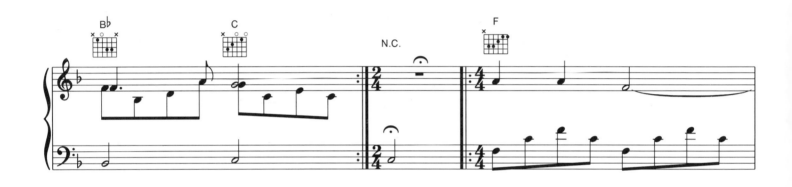

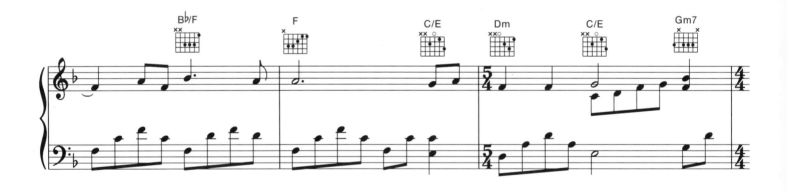

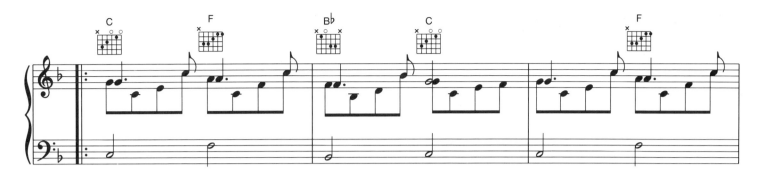

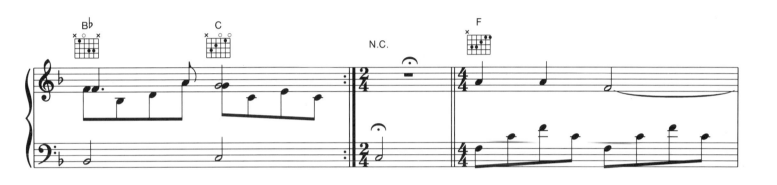

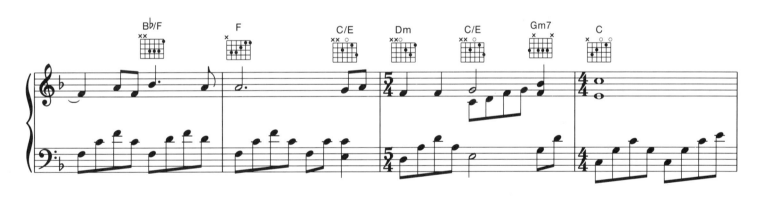

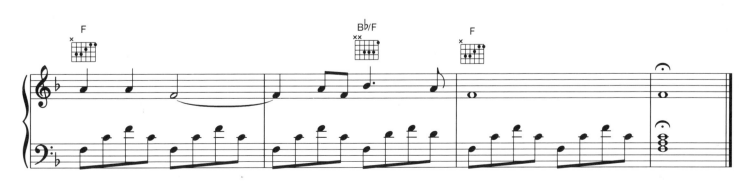

9

Caribbean Blue

Music by Enya & Nicky Ryan
Words by Roma Ryan & Arranged by Enya & Nicky Ryan

Eurus, Afer Ventus . . .

1. So the world goes
ev - ery man says

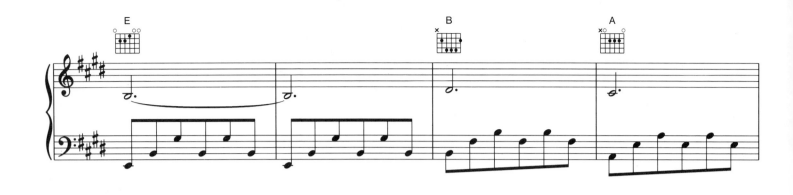

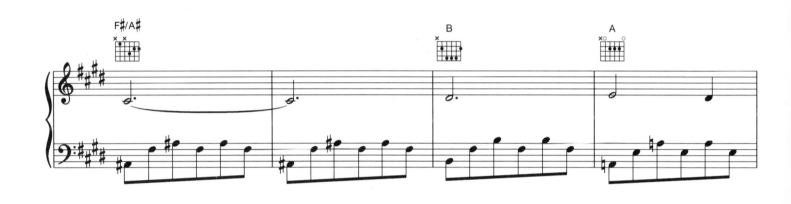

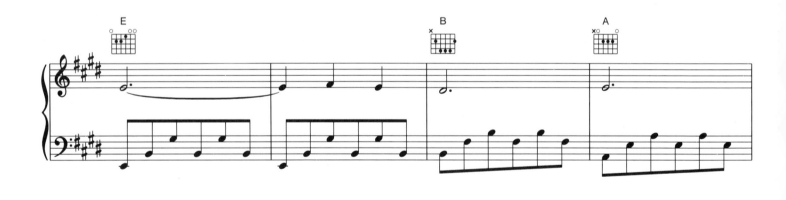

I - ma - gine sky high a - bove in Car - ib - be - an blue.

Eurus, Afer Ventus, Boreas Zephyrus, Africus . . .

How Can I Keep from Singing?

Arranged by Enya, Nicky Ryan & Roma Ryan

Ebudae

Music by Enya & Nicky Ryan
Words by Roma Ryan & Arranged by Enya & Nicky Ryan

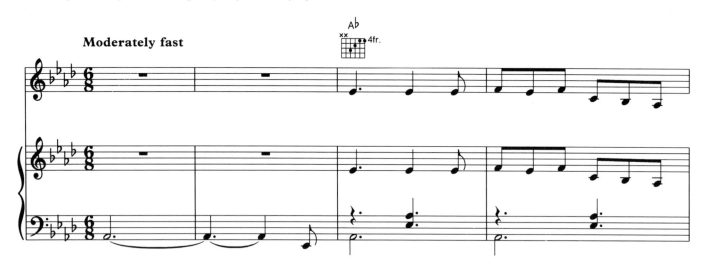

Moderately fast

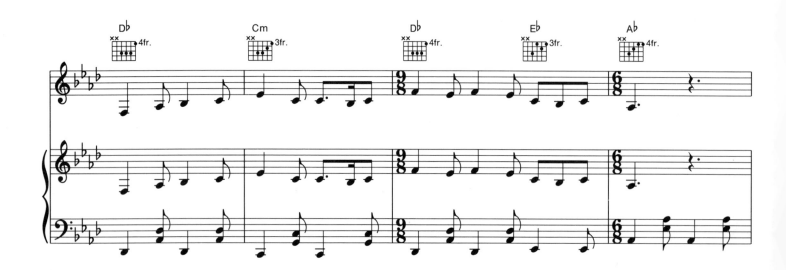

Amharc, mná - ag ob - air lá's mall san

oích, _____ Ceo - lann siad ar lae - tha geal, a

bhí, _____ Bea - lach fa - da annon's an - all a

choích. _____

Angeles

Music by Enya & Nicky Ryan
Words by Roma Ryan & Arranged by Enya & Nicky Ryan

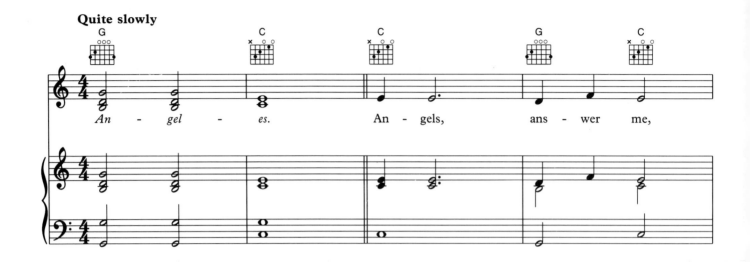

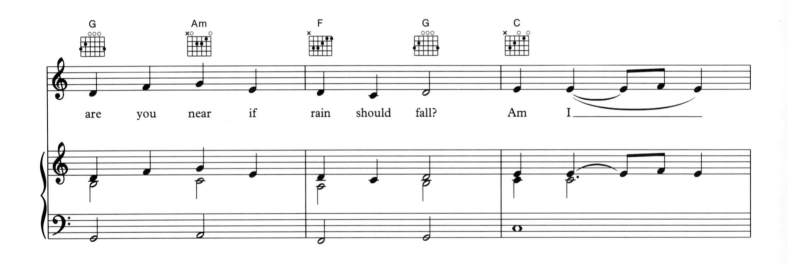

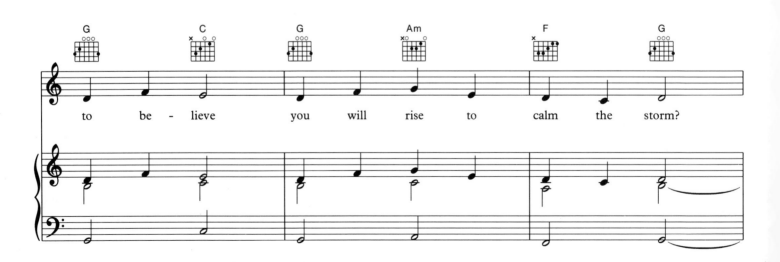

our to - mor - row. I should know hea - ven has her

way, each one giv - en mem - or - ies to

own. An - gel - es all could be should you move both

earth and sea. An - gel - es, I could feel

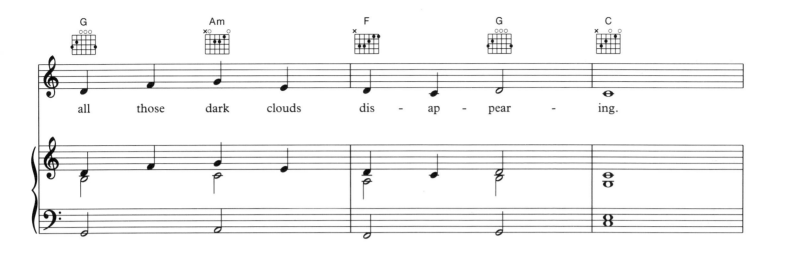

all those dark clouds dis - ap - pear - ing.

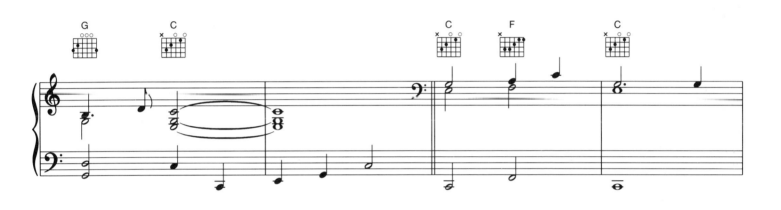

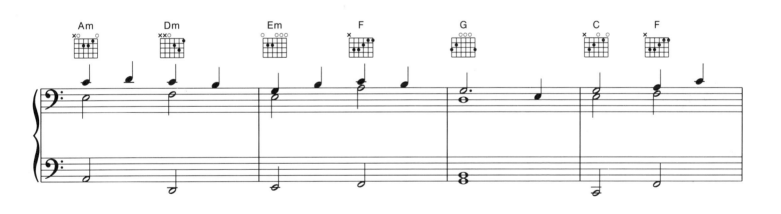

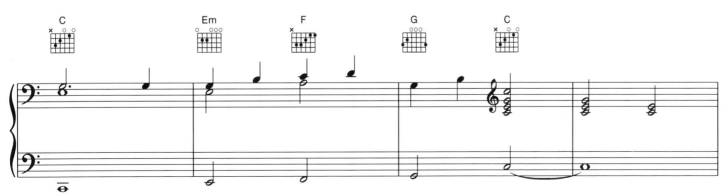

No Holly For Miss Quinn

Music by Enya & Nicky Ryan

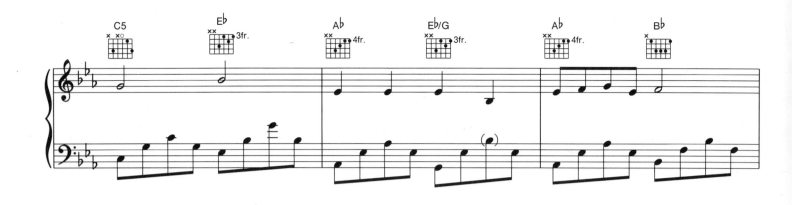

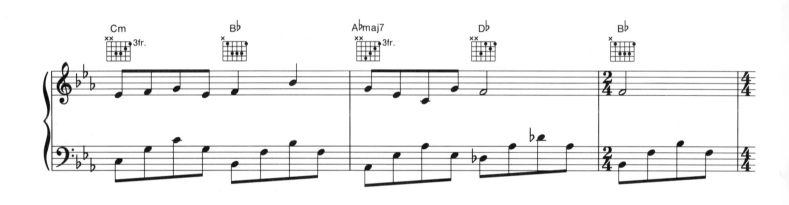

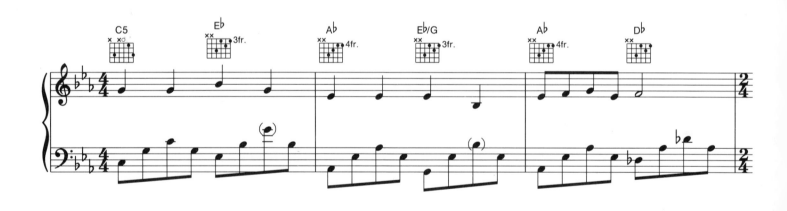

32

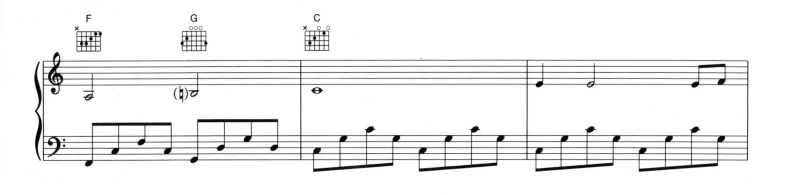

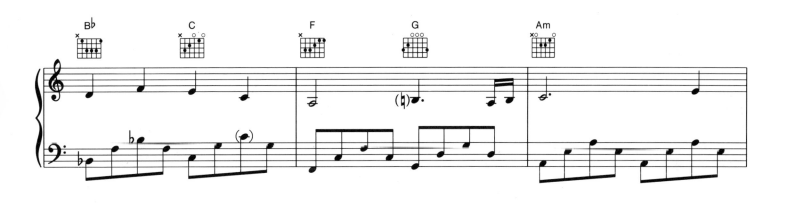

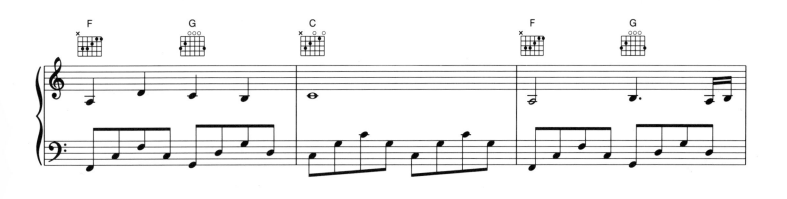

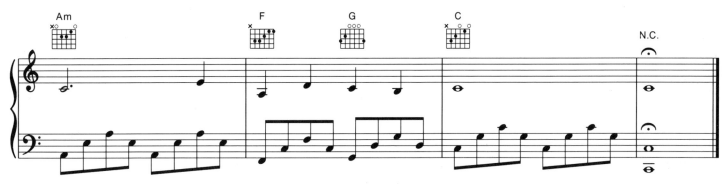

Book Of Days

Music by Enya & Nicky Ryan
Words by Roma Ryan & Arranged by Enya & Nicky Ryan

Ó oíche go hoích, mo thuras,
An bealach fada romhan.
Ó lá go lá, mo thuras,
na scéalta na mbeidh a choích.

Evacuee

Music by Enya & Nicky Ryan
Words by Roma Ryan & Arranged by Enya & Nicky Ryan

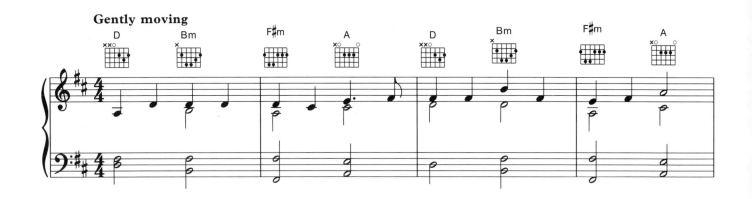

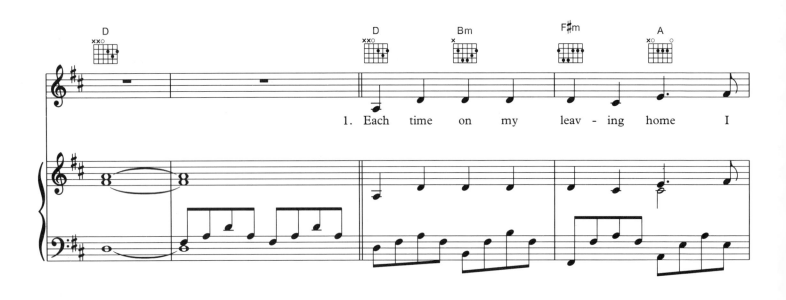

1. Each time on my leav - ing home I

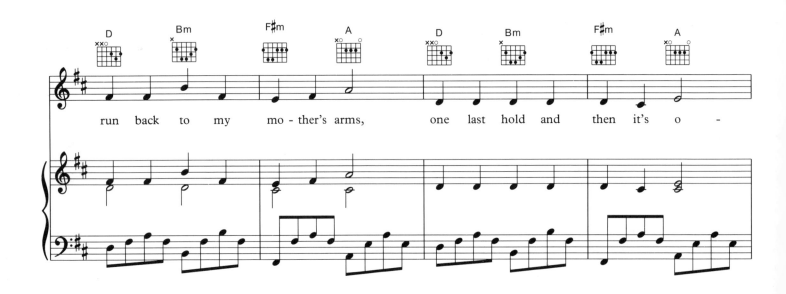

run back to my mo - ther's arms, one last hold and then it's o -

train moves on, you're gone from view, now I must wait un-

-til it's o - ver.

All I am, a

Lothlórien

Music by Enya & Nicky Ryan

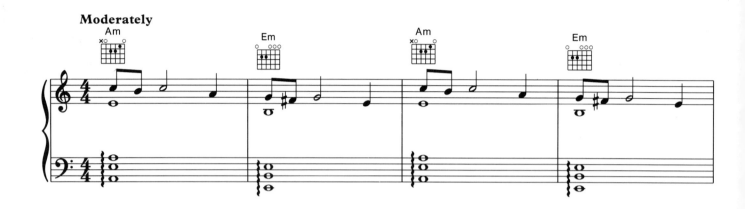

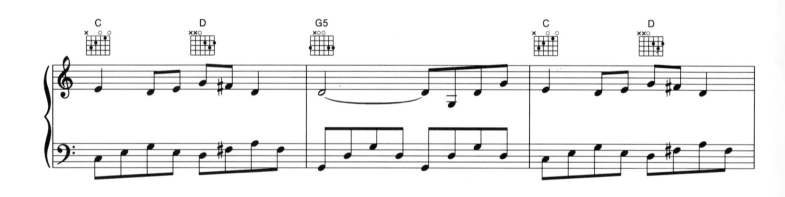

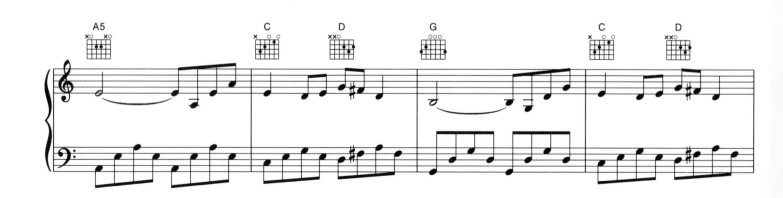

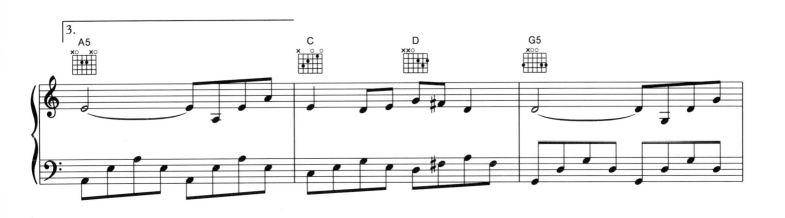

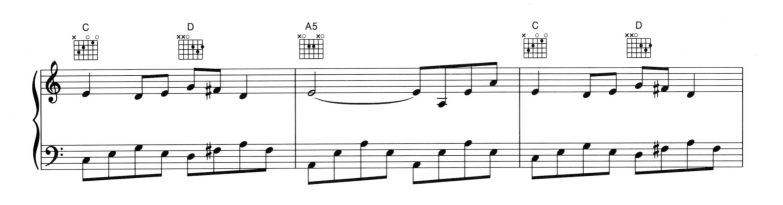

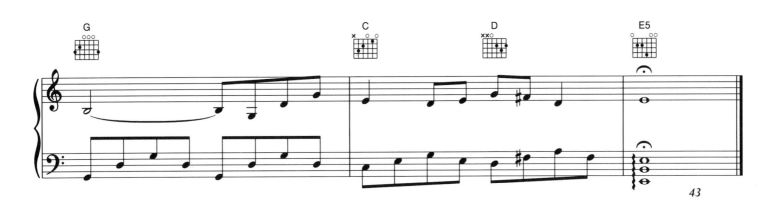

Marble Halls

Arranged by Enya, Nicky Ryan & Roma Ryan

Gently flowing

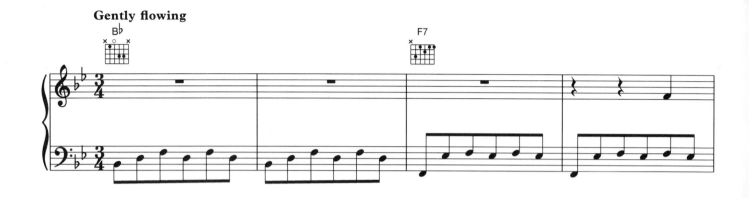

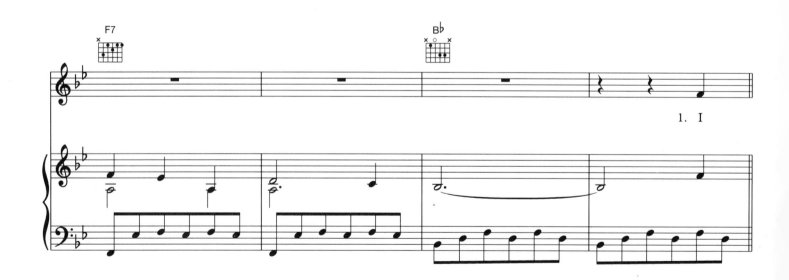

1. I

Afer Ventus

Music by Enya & Nicky Ryan
Words by Roma Ryan & Arranged by Enya & Nicky Ryan

1. Ma-re Nu-bi-um, Um-bri - el. Ma-re Im-bri-um. A - ri-el.____
2. Mi-ra-bi-le dic-tu Mi-ra - bil-i-a. Mi-ra-bi-le vi-su. Mi - ra-bil-i-a.
3. A-fer Ven-tus. Zeph-yr - us. Vol - tur - nus. Af-ri-cus.____

Et i - tur ad as - tra. Et i - tur as as - tra.

to Coda ⊕

Ma - re Un-dar-um. I - o. Ve - la._____
Sem-per vi - rent. Ro - se - tum._____
Et - es - i - ar-um. Eu - rus._____

staccato

Running verse:

Suus cuique mos. Suum cuique.
Meus mihi, suus cuique carus.
Memento, terrigena.
Memento, vita brevis.
Meus mihi, suus cuique carus.

Smaointe...
(D'Aodh Agus Do Mháire uí Dhúgain)

Music by Enya & Nicky Ryan
Words by Roma Ryan & Arranged by Enya & Nicky Ryan

1. Éist___ le mo chroí, Go___ bró - nach a
2. Aoibh - neas a___ bhí Ach___ d'imigh

choích Tá - mé cail - te gan tú 's do bhean chei -
sin sé léan___ tú Do___ fhear chei -

- le. An___ grá___ mór i do shaoil Threo - raí sí___
- le.

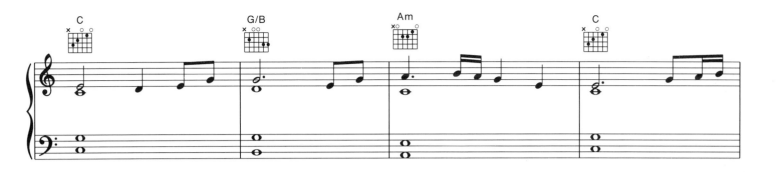

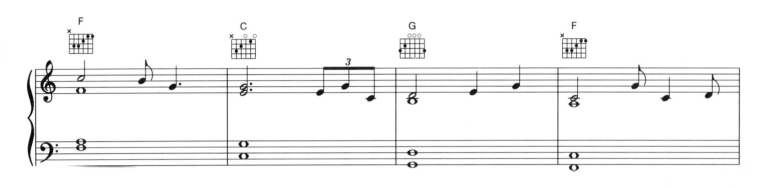

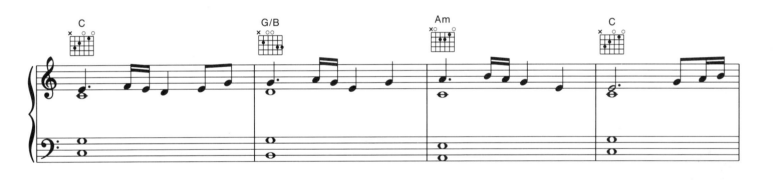

Ag

caoi - neadh ar an uaig - neas mór Na deo - ra, go bro - nach Na

gcod - ladh ins___ an uaigh___ ghlas___ chiúin Faoi shuimh - neas, go domhain.

3. Smaoin - te ar an lá Raibh sibh ar_____ mo thaobh Ag_____

ín - se sceíl Ar an doigh a_____ bhí Is_____

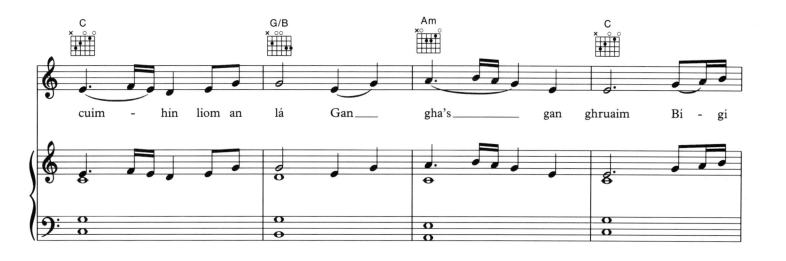

cuim - hín liom an lá   Gan___ gha's_____ gan ghruaim   Bí - gí

liom - sa i gco - naí___ Lá's_____ oích.

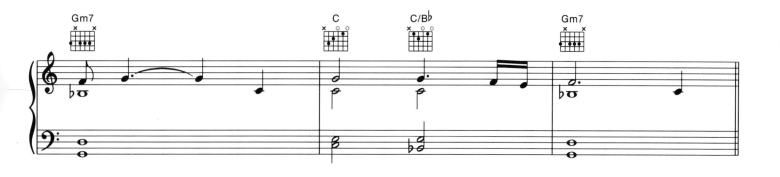

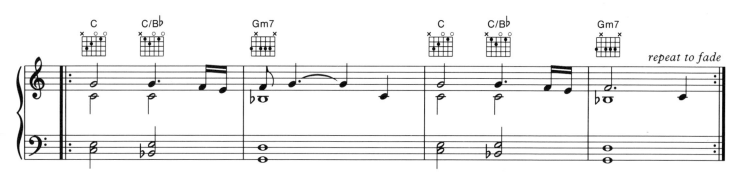

repeat to fade

Printed by J. B. Offset (Marks Tey), Colchester, Essex.